M000026730

DREAM VOYAGES

THE FASTEST, THE ULTIMATE, THE LEGENDARY

CONCORDE,   QUEEN ELIZABETH 2,   VENICE SIMPLON-
ORIENT-EXPRESS.

by

GARY C. BUCHANAN

© Gary C. Buchanan 1989

Published in the Channel Islands by
Jersey Artists Ltd   St. Martin   Jersey C.I.

For Mum and Dad

PREFACE

Dream Voyages brings together three of the world's greatest travelling experiences. This photographic anthology gives an insight into the excitement and pleasure of taking a voyage on the world's most famous train, plane and liner.

Subtitled, The Fastest, The Ultimate and The Legendary; Dream Voyages presents many previously unpublished photographs of Concorde, the greyhound of the skies, Q.E.2, truly Majesty at Sea and the Venice Simplon-Orient-Express, a rebirth of a train that caught the imagination of the world's media.

For many, the prospect of even seeing such masterpieces of excellence may be but a dream, the privilege of travelling on them pure fantasy. Dreams can come true and fantasies can be realised. The cross section of passengers is excitingly varied. Nobody should ever give up on a dream or dismiss a fantasy.

Here, I hope that the following pages can give a picturesque interpretation for many who aspire to embark on a dream voyage.

Gary C. Buchanan.
Kirkcaldy, Fife.
January 1989.

All rights reserved. No part of this publication may be reproduced, stored in a retrieval system, or transmitted in any form or by any means, electronic, mechanical, photocopy or any other information or retrieval system, without written permission from the publishers, Jersey Artists Limited.

British Library Cataloguing in Publication Data

Buchanan, Gary, 1954-
    Dream Voyages
    1. Journeys
    I. Title
    910.4

    ISBN 0-901845-14-0

By the same author
Gary C Buchanan. with George Behrend.
Night Ferry - Jersey Artists Ltd 1985
ISBN 0-901845-13-2

Printed in England by The Amadeus Press Ltd.

CONCORDE

Concorde - no other aircraft has achieved such a perfect marriage of beautiful and functional design, no other aircraft has so symbolised two nations hopes, or engaged people's passions.

Concorde is one of the wonders of the modern technical world, the world's only commercially successful supersonic passenger airliner.

Concorde is a time machine, but for anyone flying on Concorde it is still astonishing to realise that you are flying faster than a rifle bullet, while the sensation of supersonic flight is almost exactly similar to that aboard a conventional jet aircraft.

Concorde is often referred to as the Atlantic shrinker because of its sole scheduled routes across the Atlantic to New York, Miami and Washington and Barbados, establishing a unique niche in the airline world, providing travellers with the unique benefit of speed. Since April 1983, thanks to an agreement between British Airways and Cunard, Concorde has been seen in many far flung places; Rio de Janeiro, Cape Town, Hong Kong and Sydney have all welcomed the British Airways flagship enthusiastically. Goodwood Travel similarly, instituted a Concorde - Round the World programme in 1986, taking the time machine across the Pacific to the most exotic destinations most travellers can only dream of.

When Concorde first started flying commercially on 21st January 1976, the British Airways Concorde departed Heathrow at 11.00 for Bahrain in the Arabian Gulf, while an Air France Concorde departed Charles de Gaulle for Rio de Janeiro. Bahrain was chosen by British Airways as a stepping stone to Australia and the Far East. As flying rights had not been agreed into Singapore or Sydney, the supersonic flagship could go no further than Bahrain. In 1977 Concorde began operations to New York, while in the same year the supersonic aircraft started flying to Singapore via Bahrain in conjunction with Singapore Airlines - half of Concorde in British Airways livery and half in Singapore Airlines. Only three flights were made due to political difficulties with overflying rights. This service was restarted on 24th January 1979 and lasted until Singapore and Bahrain were withdrawn from the Concorde schedule on November 1st 1980.

So it was not until 1985 that a Concorde was again seen at Bahrain with one hundred passengers bound for Sydney, Queen Elizabeth 2 and half a world cruise. This time the supersonic airliner travelled via Bangkok for its refuelling stop en-route to Sydney. Clipping nearly seven hours off the scheduled subsonic flight time between London and Sydney.

Today, passengers travelling on Concorde from London, depart from one of the world's finest airport terminal buildings - Terminal 4. At check-in the prestigious 'Concorde' tags are affixed to luggage and invitations to the exclusive 'Speedwing' lounge proffered. The lounge has an air of quiet elegance, passengers settle down to read the Financial Times and the Wall Street Journal. Some sip coffee, others accept a glass of Champagne - vintage, of course! Many regular travellers acknowledge each other while some veterans still look out of the panoramic windows onto the unique delta shape wing profile of Concorde that will shortly be speeding them across the Atlantic.

A unique study showing the aerodynamic shape of Concorde and the probe which can reach temperatures of 120 degrees centigrade.

The lounge echoes with the words, "Good morning ladies and gentlemen, your Concorde supersonic flight to New York is now ready for boarding. The flying time today will be three hours and sixteen minutes and the temperature in New York is currently eleven degrees centigrade. On behalf of British Airways we wish you a very pleasant flight."

In an orderly fashion passengers present their stylish boarding cards and are shown to their allocated seats on board - no ordinary seats these, the pearl grey leather seats are more reminiscent of a Porsche than an aircraft - but then, Concorde is no ordinary aircraft.

Inside the cabin, seats are arranged two by two with an aisle down the centre. The windows are small but the aircraft flies at an altitude where the curvature of the earth can be appreciated, amazing cloudscapes enjoyed and the appearance of the "Western Sun rise" which is totally unique to Concorde. The aircraft is divided into two cabins, the forward with ten rows, the rear with fifteen, seating one hundred passengers in a one class - supersonic class - aircraft.

Soon the aircraft pushes back and slips out of the parking bay, right on time - punctuality is a must with Concorde. The cabin crew are taking the first orders for drinks and presenting the handsome menus and 'Concorde Cellar' wine lists. The menus are of world class standard and the wine list features the best growths from the finest vineyards.

On taxiing, a member of the flight crew explains that the Concorde's sporty take off requires full power, with the four Olympus engines on full reheat (burning fuel in the exhaust area to increase thrust by about 20 per cent) giving Concorde a maximum take-off speed of 225 knots, just under 260 miles per hour. One minute and twenty seconds after the start of the take off run the reheats will be cancelled and there will be a marked decrease in the rate of climb. Concorde will remain subsonic at Mach 0.95 (95 per cent of the speed of sound) until over the Bristol Channel and ready for the supersonic acceleration. In the meantime, Concorde has lined up at the end of the runway and the mighty roar

Concorde prepares to taxi from its special stand at London Heathrow Terminal 4.

6

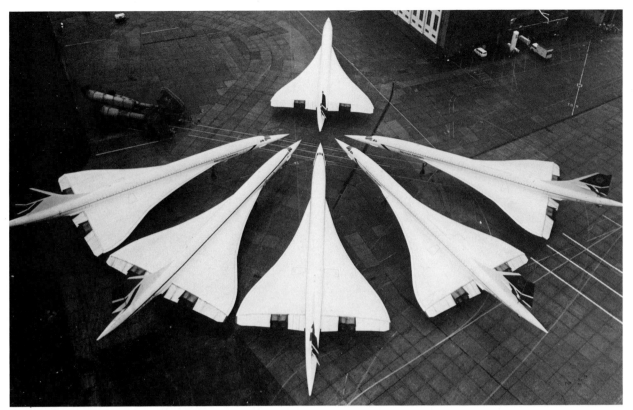

A unique display of six of British Airways' seven Concordes at their Heathrow base. These aircraft, the flagships of British Airways, will be seen in the skies well into the twenty - first century.

of the four Olympus engines (generating 38,050 lbs of thrust each) signals the start of a very special flight.

As passengers sip champagne, flying one hundred miles an hour faster than conventional aircraft - and that's before the supersonic acceleration - the most difficult decision is whether to opt for the Maine lobster poached in white wine or the grilled breast of corn fed chicken.

Soon the flight deck advise that the reheats will be engaged again, this time in pairs, to speed Concorde through the sound barrier and up to Mach 1.73, when they will be cancelled and Concorde will race up to Mach 2 (1350 miles per hour) at an altitude of 50,000 feet and continues to climb gently towards 60,000 feet. Two slight nudges herald the threshold of supersonic flight, as the reheats take effect.

A light hors d'oeuvres of poached salmon is presented on a tray boasting fine Wedgewood china and glistening crystal. Each main course is served separately following a refreshing salad. A light dessert of Crème Brulée then cheese - or both. Coffee and liqurs follow, together with a special memento of the Concorde flight.Now the south eastern tip of Newfoundland is in the distance on the right hand side. The windows have become warm to the touch and the aircraft has 'grown' eleven inches due to the airframe being heated by the airflow at Mach 2. The flight deck informs passengers that they will be returning to 'mother earth' in exactly eighty one minutes on Runway 04 Right at John F. Kennedy airport, New York. Passengers interested in visiting the flight deck can do so at this time.

At precisely three hours and eighteen minutes after leaving London (on this particular occasion) Concorde touches down on American soil. With a time difference of five hours between London and New York - Concorde arrives one hour and forty two minutes before it left!!!

The Atlantic Shrinker - yes, the Time Machine, certainly. Concorde can eliminate jet lag and bring continents closer together. It is the ultimate, the fastest and the legendary all rolled into one.

Another unique view of this unique aircraft in this historic photograph - four of them, flying in formation above England on Christmas Eve 1985.

CONCORDE MILESTONES

1962 29th November
British and French Governments sign agreement covering the joint design, development and manufacture of supersonic transport.

1969 1st October
Concorde's first supersonic flight.

1970 4th November
Mach 2 exceeded for the first time by Concorde 001.

1972 28th June
British Airways orders five and Air France orders four Concordes.

1973 20th September
Concorde 002 lands at Dallas/Fort Worth to commence first visit to the United States.

1974 13th February
Second production Concorde flies from Filton in British Airways colours.

1974 5th June
Paris/Rio/Paris; Concorde 002 flies 11,400 statute miles in 11 hours 20 minutes.

1974 17th June
First double crossing of the Atlantic.

1976 21st January
First commercial flights by British Airways London to Bahrain and Air France Paris to Rio.

1976 24th May
Transatlantic services start to Washington from London and Paris.

1977 1st November
The Queen makes her first Concorde flight returning from the Silver Jubilee tour of Canada and the Caribbean to London from Barbados in record time of 3hrs 42 minutes 5 seconds. This is less than half the normal flight time for the 4,200 journey.

1977 22nd November
Inaugural British Airways London to New York service and Air France Paris to New York.

1978 10th August
100,000 passengers carried by British Airways.

1979 12th January
The British Airways and Air France services to Washington from London and Paris extended to Dallas/Fort Worth - Concorde being leased by Braniff Airlines.

1979 16th December

A British Airways Concorde flies London to New York in 2hr 59 minutes 36 seconds.

1980 31st May

Agreement with Braniff ended, therefore service to Dallas/Fort Worth from Washington suspended.

1982 31st March

Air France service to Caracas and Rio de Janeiro discontinued.

1983 1st January

Fastest Transatlantic crossing west to east; New York to London in 2 hrs 56 minutes 35 seconds.

1984 27th March

Concorde inaugural to Miami via Washington. Henceforth a thrice weekly service.

1984 14th September

Distance record - Washington to Nice by G-BOAB 3,965 nautical miles.

1985 13th February

First commercial service London to Sydney by Concorde on charter to Cunard establishing a record time of 17 hrs and 13 mins.

1985 28th March

Concorde under a Cunard charter establishes the record between London and Cape Town of 8 hrs and 8 mins.

1985 25th April

New livery unveiled by Concorde G-BOAG returning into service. This aircraft had been out of service for a long time with much of its equipment having been removed for use in the other Concordes.

1986 21st January

Concorde celebrates ten years of commercial operations.

1986 27th July

Prime Minister, Margaret Thatcher flies to Vancouver on Concorde for the celebration of Britain at EXPO'86.

1987 12th December

Inaugural departure of British Airways Concorde scheduled service to Barbados.

Above: Concorde awaits its one hundred privileged passengers who can make last minute phone calls or enjoy cocktails in the British Airways Speedwing Lounge at Heathrow Terminal 4.

Top right: Shortly after take off Concorde's after burners can be clearly seen increasing the performance by 20%. The reheats are applied for take off and acceleration through Mach 1, the speed of sound, and remain on until around Mach 1.63 giving a powerful boost to the Rolls Royce Snecma Olympus 593 turbo jet engines as Concorde climbs to its supersonic cruising speed of Mach 2.

Bottom right: Having no flaps, Concorde lands with a marked angle of attack at speeds around 180 m.p.h. The visor is lowered to 12.5 degrees to increase visibility for the flight crew. Shortly after landing, reverse thrust is applied giving a dramatic pull up.

13

Above: The machmeter, at the front of each of Concorde's two cabins gives a visual display of speed in Mach number and miles per hour, the distance travelled and the distance to go, the outside air temperature and the altitude.

Above left: British Airways predecessor, B.O.A.C. formed a new company with the Cunard Steam-Ship Company Ltd in June 1962. This was an attempt by Cunard to maintain a presence in Transatlantic travel.

Below left: The inaugural service by Concorde to the United States. Both British Airways and Air France celebrated the age of supersonic services to Washington Dulles Airport on 24th May 1976.

As the sun rises over Concorde's visor, the world's only commercial supersonic aircraft prepares for its morning departure from London to New York's J.F.K. The passengers will beat the sun as they race across the Atlantic arriving some eighty minutes before they left!

The evening departure of Concorde from London to New York allows a full day in London prior to departure and in just over three hours passengers have travelled almost 3,500 miles and can enjoy a show on Broadway having had their pre-theatre dinner in the best restaurant between London and New York.

An interesting angle on Concorde G-BOAA showing the unique delta wing that was instrumental in the development of supersonic flight.

Concorde powers through the skies as this unusual angle shows - beating the sun and the clock.

A spectacular view of the first British pre-production Concorde at Nairobi. Since the introduction of world wide charters, Concorde has been seen at over one hundred airports.

18

Concorde's slim interior is compact, but not cramped. The pearl grey leather seats are as much a feature of the best sports cars as the world's fastest civil aircraft. The two cabins, all one class, offer ten rows of seats, two abreast in the forward cabin and fifteen rows of two abreast in the rear cabin.

A splendid view of the flight deck. The captain sits on the left, the senior first officer on the right and the engineer in the foreground in front of the systems control panel.

An interesting view of Concorde's visor lowered to the 5 degree position.

Concorde enjoys many Royal patrons. Here, Her Majesty, Queen Elizabeth the Queen Mother discusses the flying experience with Captain Brian Walpole prior to her special circumnavigation of Britain to celebrate Her eightieth birthday.

Her Royal Highness the Duchess of York experiences the thrill of sitting in the Captain's seat while Senior First Officer Jock Lowe demonstrates the control systems on the ground.

Concorde G-BOAG climbing to its supersonic acceleration point of Mach 0.95 at 25,000 feet. On board passengers are enjoying cocktails and canapés.

Seen flying in formation with the Red Arrow Hawks at R.A.F. Fairford in July 1985, Concorde is a regular welcome visitor at air shows around the world. Demonstration flying ceased in 1988.

At 58,000 feet - eleven miles high, Concorde enjoys the freedom of the skies. Not only is she flying five miles higher than subsonic aircraft, but she also flies above turbulent weather - giving its privileged passengers a smooth journey.

Passengers are invited to visit the flight deck of Concorde during the flight; though both time and space are restricted, but few passengers refuse such an experience.

The photograph of the century. Concorde, under the command of Captain Leney, Queen Elizabeth 2 with Captain Bob Arnott at the helm and the Red Arrows display team. A photograph which evokes a great sense of pride.

An aerial view of Concorde with the Red Arrow Hawks. The precision flying and co-ordination is clearly evident.

Concorde G-BOAG landing at Miami. The three times weekly flight from London via Washington has proved very popular with cruise passengers joining their ships in either the Port of Miami or Port Everglades.

With the nose in the fully down position of 12.5 degrees Concorde G-BOAG touches down in Miami just six and a half hours after leaving London.

Concorde's sweeping delta wing and thin fuselage give it a unique place in the skies around the world.

The aerodynamic shape of Concorde is clearly demonstrated from this angle. The Rolls Royce/Snecma Olympus 593 turbo jet engines each give a maximum take off thrust of 38,050 lbs.

Faster than a rifle bullet and not a ripple on the champagne. An experience without equal in the world of travel today - and tomorrow!

Concorde G-BOAG cruising at 58,000 feet at a speed of Mach 2.0 equivalent to 1,320 m.p.h. Here the curvature of the earth can be clearly seen.

The six members of Concorde's specially trained cabin crew know the whims and desires of the Concorde passenger and excellent care and attention are assured in this diamond in the sky.

APERITIFS & COCKTAILS

Sweet and Dry Vermouth
Campari Soda · Americano · Negroni
Medium Dry Sherry · Dry Martini · Gin · Vodka
Bloody Mary · Old Fashioned · Manhattan
Sours—Whisky · Gin · Brandy
Gin Fizz

Highballs—Whisky · Brandy · Gin · Rum

Champagne Cocktail

—∗—

SPIRITS

Whisky—Scotch · Bourbon · Rye · Malt
Gin · Vodka

—∗—

BEERS

Ale · Lager

—∗—

SELECTION OF SOFT DRINKS

Mineral Water

—∗—

WINES

CHAMPAGNE

Cuvée de René Lalou Millésimé

René Lalou is Mumm's finest cuvée—a blend of the choicest black and white
grapes of vintage years only, gathered in the most famous
vineyards of the Champagne district.

WHITE BURGUNDY

One of the following excellent Burgundy wines will be available

Chablis Premier Cru 1984

Made from the classic Chardonnay grape this excellent Chablis from the
renowned house of Sichel has a dry character with a perfect balance of
elegance and body. The wine has the typical greenish tinge
found in all great Chablis.
or
Meursault les Casse Tetes 1985

The white wines of Meursault have a reputation for being
both dry yet full—an unusual combination.
The 1985 Meursault les Casse Tetes of Roland Thevenin with its
typical Chardonnay nose and round somewhat nutty palate, is an elegant
example of this popular wine, offering freshness yet perfect balance.

RED BORDEAUX

Château Mouton—Baronne-Philippe 1981

From the vineyards of Baron-Philippe de Rothschild,
this fine example of the 1981 vintage is already showing the
brilliant ruby colour, the rich blackcurrant fruit and the 'cigar box' fragrance
so typical of the red wines from the Pauillac Commune of Bordeaux.

—∗—

LIQUEURS

Remy Martin Napoleon Cognac
Drambuie · Cointreau · Coffee Liqueur · Irish Cream Liqueur
Taylor's Vintage Port

Jamaica Macanudo cigars

APERITIFS · CHAMPAGNE

·

Canapés
Goose liver pâté with truffle, shrimps and caviar barquette

LUNCH

LOBSTER AND MANGO SALAD

A refreshing combination of lobster and fresh mango flavoured with
lemon and mint dressing

—∗—

ASSORTED GRILLED FILLETS

Fillets of veal, lamb and beef. Seared on a hot griddle and garnished with
sautéed capsicums, braised fennel, tomato stuffed with
spinach and buttered root vegetables

POACHED SALMON IN CHAMPAGNE SAUCE

Fresh salmon poached in white wine with herbs, then finished in
cream and champagne sauce. Garnished with braised fennel,
tomato stuffed with spinach and buttered root vegetables

COLD COLLATION

As a lighter alternative may we suggest our cold plate of tender,
grain-fed breast of chicken, ham and roast breast of duck
Garnished with watercress and tomato with coleslaw salad

—∗—

SALAD BOWL

Mixed seasonal salad featuring oak leaf lettuce, curly endive,
portulac herb, french beans and yellow and red pimento
Served with mustard vinaigrette

DESSERT

Delicate mousse flavoured with bitter-sweet chocolate,
garnished with pirouline wafers

—∗—

ASSORTED CHEESE

A selection of French Brie, English Stilton and
Farmhouse Leicester cheese, served with
crackers, butter and crudités

—∗—

COFFEE

Coffee or decaffeinated coffee served with a selection of friandises

---

The menus on board Concorde reflect the type of passenger who flies on the world's most sophisticated aircraft. Subtle combinations of the finest produce from around the world are complimented by wines from the world's finest cellars.

Concorde prepares for take off. Full throttle is applied and reheats selected. Soon Vr is reached at around 225 m.p.h. and Concorde leaves the ground giving its passengers the most spirited take off in civil aviation.

QUEEN ELIZABETH 2

'Travelling', wrote Guy de Maupassant, 'is the gateway through which one escapes from reality to step into a dream'. Nowhere could this statement be more apt than crossing the Atlantic Ocean by the luxury liner Queen Elizabeth 2.

Brass-bound trunks piled high by the boat-train at Waterloo Station ostentatiously marked 'not wanted on voyage', railway porters settling down their particular passengers, handkerchiefs fluttering, and the air thick with cigar smoke and expensive perfume. If you can recall this kind of scene, then you must be able to reel off the names of those pre-war liners that took the conspicuously wealthy out on to the high seas from Southampton Water. The Mauritania, Aquitania and probably the greatest of them all The Queen Mary, who made her maiden voyage on 27th May 1936. More than fifty years on, the sole relic of that glorious era plys the mighty Atlantic for six months every year, cruising the warmer waters of the globe for the remainder.

Q.E.2 was built for the swinging Sixties, surviving the economic shock of the Seventies she entered the Eighties with a new sense of purpose. Not so much to recapture an age which has long since gone, but to attract a new generation of travellers who can combine business with pleasure, and who prefer grace to pace across the mighty Atlantic.

People who cross the Atlantic by sea are those who actually have a sense of the distance they have travelled and hence the sheer size of the ocean, not to mention respect for the powerful sea. As the mighty Queen slips gently from her berth at Southampton, waved at from well-wishers and hooted at by lesser sea-faring craft, first time travellers are exploring the twelve decks, which house the four restaurants, two indoor and two outdoor pools, 530-seat theatre, many shops and numerous bars, while the cognoscenti sip fine champagne in the privacy of their staterooms and penthouses.

On Transatlantic crossings, Q.E.2 operates as a two class ship. Transatlantic class offers medium priced accommodation and good food in the Mauritania restaurant. About half the ships passengers elect to travel First class and can select from a wide range of staterooms from the more modest on two deck to the delightful penthouse suites on the Signal and Sports deck. First class restaurants range from the impressive Columbia through the intimate Princess Grill to the ultimate in haute cuisine on the high seas, the Queens Grill.

In all other respects passengers enjoy much the same facilities - round-the-clock service and a choice of sparkling entertainment and almost non-stop activity, for which stamina is probably the most essential requirement.

You can start the day with a work-out in the gym, or a gentle jog around the boat deck - five times round equals one mile. Breakfast follows - the menu is two closely printed pages featuring British, American

R.M.S. Queen Mary leaves Southampton for the last time on 31st October 1967, bound for Long Beach, California, where she attracts many new guests in her role as 'Hotel Queen Mary'. Sadly the fate of R.M.S. Queen Elizabeth was not as kind. In January 1972 the grand old lady was totally destroyed by fire in Hong Kong harbour.

Under construction in 1967 at John Brown (Clydebank) Ltd, Q.E.2, then called simply 736 (the shipyard's order-book number for the new Cunarder) occupied the same berth from which the two earlier Queens had been launched. The launch of Q.E.2 occurred on 20th September 1967, when Her Majesty Queen Elizabeth II uttered the words, "I name this ship Queen Elizabeth the Second. May God bless her and all who sail in her."

936 feet long and 105 feet wide, thirteen decks accommodating almost 3,000 passengers and crew. Queen Elizabeth 2 is truly Majesty at Sea. Here her ten Port side lifeboats above Boat Deck can be clearly seen. The new profile funnel and casing is also well detailed.

and Continental choices. The next selection ranges from aerobic classes at the Golden Door Health Club to bridge classes, to lectures on the great liners of yesteryear, you can even learn computing during the five day crossing to the Big Apple.

Pre-lunch cocktails - a different bar every lunch and dinner, such is the choice - are followed by more decisions from the extensive lunch time menus. Lighter, appetising creations are featured for the weight conscious - and who isn't after such a bevy of gastronomic delights including: Caviar, Paté de Foie Gras, fresh Maine lobster followed by Crown of English spring lamb and crêpes Suzette to finish.

Afternoon activities range from trap shooting, shuffle board or golf to classical concerts in the mighty Queens Room or perusing the excellent range of texts in the library. Afternoon tea is a religion on Q.E.2 and a sumptuous range of pastries usually pass untouched as passengers think about dinner - all too imminent.

The evening generally starts with either a formal cocktail party or another round of the cocktail bars. In the Grill Rooms passengers may choose whatever they want for dinner - within reason, but only just - some passengers spend the entire crossing working their way through the 150lbs of caviar carried on board. Some enjoy sampling from the 25,000 bottles of fine wines in the ship's cellars. Service is always attentive and friendly and your name well remembered for your next crossing.

There is entertainment and dancing every night in the Queens Room and the Grand Lounge plus nightly dancing in the Theatre Bar, a pianist in the Yacht Club, and for those who can survive the course, late night dancing in the sumptuous Club Lido with sliding 'magrodome' roof for romancing under the stars.

Not a photographic trick. This aerial view was taken as Q.E.2 prepares to dock at Southampton in April 1987. Concorde overflew Q.E.2 at low altitude giving the photographer a unique opportunity to catch 'grace

and pace'. On board Q.E.2 was Her Royal Highness The Princess of Wales and hundreds of Southampton children. Later that day Queen Elizabeth 2 set sail for New York for the first time as a motor ship.

Each evening, travelling westbound, clocks are put back one hour, eliminating jet lag and giving the night time revellers that extra hour to recover before the whole routine starts again. The complete crossing takes just under five days and surely there can be no greater climax to a journey than sailing up the Hudson River, past the Statue of Liberty, with the unique Manhattan skyline silhouetted in the morning sun. Shortly 'the only way to cross, elegantly' experience will be over, five days seem like five hours, but it is the luxury of time that Q.E.2 is all about. You are sealed off from routine as surely as if you had left the face of the earth. Q.E.2 really does offer a gateway through which you can escape from reality and step into a dream.

Queen Elizabeth 2 represents one of the most complex integrations of design and machinery ever attempted by man - a vessel capable of going almost anywhere on the globe covered by oceans, with nearly 2,000 passengers and 1,000 crew at a speed in excess of 30 miles an hour in the height of luxury. Today at the mid-point in her career she still remains ultra-modern and an engineering refit in 1987 has ensured her smooth sailing well into the twenty-first century.

Queen Elizabeth 2 alongside the Q.E.2 Terminal at Southampton. Here a typical provisions list for a Transatlantic voyage would include such varied items as 25,000 pounds of beef, 22,000 pounds of fresh fruit, 150 pounds of caviar and 1,000 bottles of champagne. All have to be loaded during the short 'turn round' of Q.E.2 - this can be as short as eight hours.

Queen Elizabeth 2 Milestones

1964 30th December

The contract to build a new Cunarder was signed by Sir John Brocklebank, then Chairman of Cunard, and Lord Aberconway, Chairman of John Brown's.

1965 4th July

On American Independence Day and 125th anniversary of the first Cunarder, Britannia's maiden voyage in 1840, the first prefabricated section of the keel for hull number 736 was laid at John Brown's shipyard, Clydebank.

1967 20th September

"I name this ship Queen Elizabeth the Second. May God bless her and all who sail in her." Her Majesty Queen Elizabeth II named the new liner, not after herself, as some would have claimed, but simply Queen Elizabeth 2 - or the second ship to bear that name. Apparently, it was an impulse decision on the part of Her Majesty that no one, not even at Cunard's headquarters, had expected, for it had been secretly agreed that the ship would be named simply Queen Elizabeth. Ahead lay a year of fitting out. The new Queen was to fill two roles - that of Transatlantic Express liner, and leisure cruise ship.

1968 December

Q.E.2 sails gracefully away from Gourock, Scotland, with 600 John Brown's men on board, still doing final fitting out work.

1969 April

Cunard Line accepts delivery of the new ship from the builders. She sails on a "preview cruise" from the U.K.

1969 2nd May

Maiden Transatlantic crossing from Southampton. Official visit from Her Majesty Queen Elizabeth II and the Duke of Edinburgh prior to sailing.

1969 Maiden arrival in New York. The Q.E.2 was greeted by Mayor John Lindsay.

1970 June

Q.E.2 crosses from Southampton to New York in 3 days, 20 hours and 42 minutes, averaging 30.36 knots.

1970 October

Q.E.2's first long cruise - 37 days to North America, Africa and South America.

1971 9th January

In the Grenadines, Q.E.2 rescues 501 passengers and crew from the burning wreck of the 19,828 ton French Line cruise ship Antilles, and lands them in Barbados.

1975 January

Q.E.2's first world cruise.

1975 May

Q.E.2 meets "Operation Tall Ships" in Tenerife, Canary Islands.

1977 Britannia Restaurant is converted into Tables of the World the largest of Q.E.2's four restaurants. The Ultra deluxe Queen Elizabeth and Queen Mary suites were added. The grill room became the Princess Grill and the 736 Club (formerly a discotheque) was transformed into the Queens Grill. At the same time the underused 24 hour Coffee Shop was reworked into the kitchen space and the Queens Grill Lounge, one of the most elegant and understated rooms afloat. The forward Lookout Bar on Upper Deck was sadly, changed to become the kitchens for the Tables of the World Restaurant. On Upper Deck Midships the Portside Promenade and Library was changed into a full Casino and named the Players Club, meanwhile the Theatre Bar was transformed into a disco.

1979   Q.E.2 did her tenth World Cruise, including a maiden transit of the Suez Canal, and the greatest number of passengers ever.

1982   May

Q.E.2 was requisitioned by Her Majesty's Government for service as a troop ship. The requisition came as Q.E.2 was crossing between Philadelphia and Southampton. When Q.E.2 arrived in Southampton, it took only seven days to convert her into a troop ship, complete with helicopter landing pads. All furniture, artworks, slot-machines, pianos and plants were offloaded and placed into storage.

1982   August

Q.E.2 sets sail for engine trials after a nine week refit to reconvert her to passenger service. The Golden Door Spa at Sea was added, the Q.4 Room (the swinging first class nightclub) was converted into the Club Lido. Q.E.2's hull was painted pebble grey - not a pretty sight! The ship sailed Transatlantic for the first time since the Falklands service.

1983   April

First Transatlantic crossing with British Airways supersonic Concorde.

1984   January

A huge 'magrodome' sliding glass roof was added to the Club Lido indoor/outdoor recreation centre. The Reading Room was converted into an I.B.M. Computer Centre.

1984   Cunard signs $40 million contract with British Airways. More than 10,000 passengers travelling round trip one way Concorde, one way Queen Elizabeth 2.

1984   June

The first sea-going branch of Harrods was added.

1984   December

The Columbia Restaurant was refurbished.

1986   May

A Royal touch, as Her Majesty Queen Elizabeth, the Queen Mother, visits Q.E.2 in Southampton for the Cunarder, Queen Mary's fiftieth anniversary celebrations.

1986   October

Q.E.2 features her last voyage as a steam ship, prior to entering the Lloyd Werft shipyard in Bremerhaven, Germany for her six month long refit.

1987   29th April

Her Royal Highness The Princess of Wales joins five hundred Hampshire schoolchildren on a short trip to the Isle of Wight and back, before passengers embark on the inaugural Transatlantic crossing from Southhampton to New York under diesel power, arriving 4th May. A flotilla of small craft escorted the 'new Q.E.2 past the Statue of Liberty.

14th   December

Her Royal Highness, Queen Elizabeth the Queen Mother, lunches on board Q.E.2 for a special 21st Birthday celebration of the launch of the mighty liner.

1989   28th March

Q.E.2 begins a three month charter in Yokohama in Japan.

Departing from Southampton, the port holes of Six Deck, just above the water line, where staff accommodation and the ship's hospital are situated, are evident to the keen eye. Rising ten decks, the deluxe penthouse accommodation and suites occupy the Sports and Signal Decks.

An impressive view of Queen Elizabeth 2, anchored off Malaga during a recent cruise to the Iberian peninsula. Approaching by one of the ships tenders, the mighty proportions of the great ship become awe-inspiring.

A unique photograph of the ship's company. Taken in New York before the last voyage under steam in 1986. Many of the 1,000 members of the ship's company fill One Deck, forward; Quarter Deck and Upper Deck: Captain Lawrence Portet and his officers resplendent in their summer uniforms.

Captain Alan Bennell, the present master of Q.E.2 on the wings of the bridge prior to docking at Pier 93. Captain Bennell insists on meeting all passengers at least once in the course of a Transatlantic crossing.

The author and master of the Q.E.2 Captain Alan Bennell, during a recent Transatlantic voyage.

Above: Outward bound from New York, Q.E.2 passes the Statue of Liberty and heads out towards the Verrazano Narrows Bridge. The towering mast complements the massive Cunard red funnel. The traditional slate grey hull is preferred by many to the lighter pebble grey she sported briefly from August 1982 to June 1983.

Left: A spectacular aerial view of Queen Elizabeth 2 sailing down the East River with the unique Manhattan skyline in the background. Many passengers crowd the boat deck and sports deck-forward to witness this impressive sight.

A unique view of the bridge. On the left can be seen the tiny ship's wheel while an officer of the watch monitors the progress of Q.E.2 from this modern day crows nest.

The navigators panel on the bridge of Q.E.2. State of the art electronics guide the world's only superliner across the oceans.

An engineer keeps a watchful eye in the control room. Totally transformed during the 1987 refit from steam turbine to diesel electric propulsion, the engineering team monitor the progress of the ship's mechanics in an air of calm efficiency.

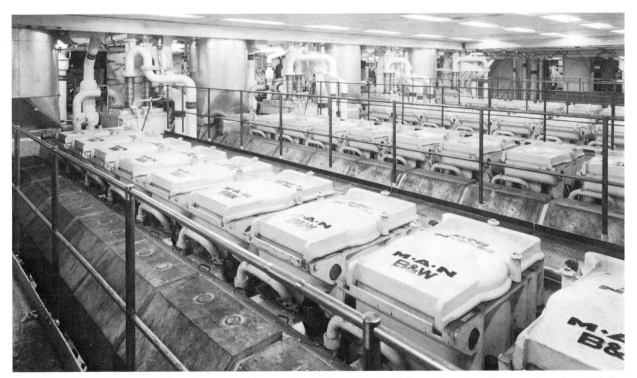

A view of the Engine Room after the conversion to diesel electric propulsion. The nine, four stroke, nine cylinder diesel engines are named Alpha to India. The engine room is unmanned and remotely controlled from the control room.

Above: Q.E.2 transverses the Panama Canal. This photograph shows the largest ship to transverse the canal approaching Gaillard Cut from Gatun Lake (one of the largest man-made freshwater lakes in the world). From here Q.E.2 continues to the pair of Miraflores locks which mark the end of the transit of the Panama Canal on the Pacific side. The size of Q.E.2 makes any transit of the canal an adventure, the maximum clearance is only thirty inches per side. The liner is 963 feet in length and the locks are 1,100 feet.

Left: During the 1987 refit in Bremerhaven two new five blade propellers were fitted maintaining Q.E.2 as the largest, most powerful twin screw vessel in the world. The vast bulk of the hull is awe-inspiring.

The mighty Cunarder is a regular visitor to the Norwegian Fjords. The spectacular land of the midnight sun plays host to Q.E.2 providing a dramatic backcloth for the elegant lines of the 68,000 ton liner.

The North Atlantic can be the most inhospitable sea in the world. On 27th May 1987, Q.E.2 endured a force ten hurricane, Captain Portet maintained a steady course despite seas as high as 37 feet. Arrival in Southampton was on schedule.

The Club Lido pool on Quarter Deck (aft) during a warm weather cruise. A buffet style lunch can be enjoyed in the sun while Queen Elizabeth 2 heads for her next exotic port.

The Club Lido pool is an all weather escape. The sliding Magrodome roof, fitted in 1983, can open in warm climates or close in cooler climates (as shown). The Club Lido has a dance floor, bar, disco, food serving area, pool and comfortable lounge chairs.

The world's greatest liner in the world's greatest harbour. Q.E.2 attracts a flotilla of smaller craft as she prepares to dock in Sydney during her world cruise.

The Mid-Ships Lobby. For many their first view of Q.E.2. Here, on Two Deck forward, most passengers join the liner and are directed to their cabins and staterooms while a pianist plays familiar and appropriate melodies.

An A grade cabin in traditional style. Each of the penthouse suites have individual designs and furnishings - from classical to ultra-modern.

Gala Dinner

Hors d'Oeuvre

Russian Malossol Caviar served with chopped Onion and Egg, Sour Cream

Jumbo Shrimp Cocktail, Sauce Américaine

Chilled Honeydew Melon with Parma Ham

Soups

Mock Turtle Soup with Truffle Essence and Cheese Sticks

Cream of Fresh Mushroom Soup

Crème Vichyssoise

Crustaceans

Fresh Cold Maine Lobster Queen Elizabeth 2
Served with Sauce Cardinal

Sherbet

Lime Sherbet

Main Dishes

Roast American Prime Rib au jus
with French Green Beans and Baked Potato with Sour Cream and Chives

Medallions of Veal served on Bell Pepper Stripes with Morels and Gorgonzola Cream

Pointrine de Poulet Louis XV. Breast of Chicken filled with Crabmeat Mousse
Baked in the oven with Julienne of Vegetables and served on a Bed of Fresh Spinach
with Sauce Newbourg

Vegetables & Potatoes

French Green Beans   Carrots Vichy   Cauliflower

Baked   Pont Neuf   Parsley   Boiled Potatoes

Salad

Caesar Salad à la Mode du Chef

Desserts, Ice Cream & Dessert Sauces

Hazelnut Soufflé with Strawberry Cream   Parfait Diplomate
Fresh Strawberries with Vanilla Ice Cream and Whipped Cream   Lime Sherbert

Ice Cream   Vanilla   Chocolate   Walnut

Dessert Sauces   Caramel   Chocolate

★ ★ ★ ★ ★

Fresh Fruit in Season   Assorted Cheese with Crackers

Freshly Brewed Decaffeinated Coffee   Coffee   Tea

Welcome Aboard

Above: The Grand Lounge is the largest public room afloat. Here, world class cabaret stars perform in the most famous club between the West End and Broadway.

Left: Q.E.2 sailing up the North River to the Cunard Terminal. Her maiden arrival on May 7th 1969 was accompanied by a flotilla of Coast Guard cutters, fire boats, tugs, ferries and yachts.

The Columbia Restaurant is the largest restaurant for first class passengers. (Q.E.2 has two classes only on Transatlantic sailings.) The ambiance is lively and the service attentive.

The Princess Grill on Quarter Deck, offers first class passengers intimate surroundings for both lunch and dinner. This is the smallest restaurant on Q.E.2.

The Queen's Grill lounge is a focal point pre lunch and dinner. Afternoon tea is served here for penthouse accommodation passengers. In the evening it is transformed into a catwalk - displaying some amazing fashions.

A popular evening haunt is the Yacht Club bar, situated on Upper Deck. Here, on the right, can be seen a white piano with a glass top and surrounding glass bar. Favourite melodies are played through to the early hours.

The Queen's Grill - the ultimate in luxury. The top restaurant on Queen Elizabeth 2. Here the expert team of restaurant managers and staff cater to every passenger's culinary whims and caprices. Many regular travellers don't even consult the menu, such is their confidence in the chef's desire to please.

The Mauritania Restaurant on Upper Deck seats all Transatlantic class passengers in two sittings. Prints depicting early days of Cunard adorn the walls together with this oil painting of the great Mauritania.

The Queen's Room. One of the most elegant afloat. Nightly cabaret and dancing is enjoyed here and is the venue for the Captain's cocktail party for first class passengers.

A grade AA cabin - the 'Queen Anne' suite on Signal Deck reflects the truly luxurious surroundings of the penthouse accommodation offered on Q.E.2.

An interesting photograph of the stern of Q.E.2 showing the open pool on One Deck; the Club Lido (with the Magrodome roof closed) on Quarter Deck; paddle tennis courts, shuffleboard, table tennis and golf driving nets on Upper Deck; Boat Deck and the new enclosed sun trap on Sports Deck.

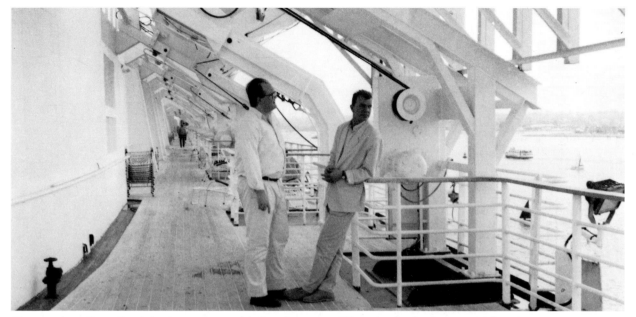

The spacious Boat Deck is shown here with Southampton Water in the background. Five times around the U-shaped track equals one mile and is used extensively by joggers. Other passengers prefer to amble around or quietly enjoy the ever changing scenery.

THE ONLY WAY TO CROSS

One hundred and fifteen hours after leaving New York, Queen Elizabeth 2 arrives in her port of registry - Southampton. The open expanse of deck towards the stern have never been equalled in any other liner.

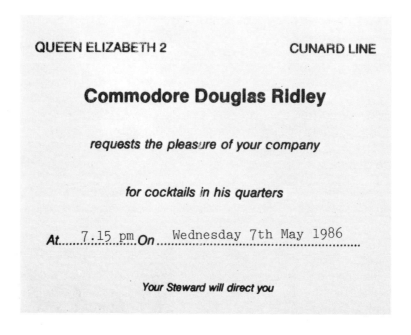

QUEEN ELIZABETH 2   CUNARD LINE

Commodore Douglas Ridley

requests the pleasure of your company

for cocktails in his quarters

At   7.15 pm   On   Wednesday 7th May 1986

Your Steward will direct you

The Venice Simplon
Orient-Express

It was known in its gilded heyday as the Train of Kings and the King of Trains. It also transported in regal splendour Diplomats and Duchesses, Maharajahs and Moguls, Courtesans and Couriers, private eyes and spies. Thundering across Empires to the edge of Asia, the Orient Express was the most celebrated train in history. It retired in May 1977, aged 94, a shrunken outcast of the hurry-up age. Then in May 1982, it rose again in all its pristine opulence as a regularly scheduled 'Train de Luxe', plying between London and Venice.

The 'Magic carpet to the East' was the brainchild of Belgian, George Nagelmakers, who thought of bringing the American luxury Pullman boudoir to Europe. His Paris to Constantinople (Istanbul) journey time was 81 hours and 40 minutes, and it was a luxury train from the outset. Also nicknamed the 'Land Liner', the Orient Express has been romantically mentioned in fiction. Maurice Dèkobra's 'the Madonna of the Sleeping Cars', Agatha Christie's 'Murder on the Orient Express', Graham Greene's 'Stamboul Train' to name but a few.

The 1060 mile journey from London to Venice takes a leisurely 30 hours, departing from London's Victoria Station at 11.00 am every Thursday and Sunday. From the moment you make the airline style check-in you get the feeling it is a grand occasion. The hustle and bustle of London is replaced with an opulent calm as you enter the English section of the train. Nine chocolate and cream Pullman cars, each shining and polished like a new toy reassures the most dubious traveller as he makes himself comfortable in the elegantly panelled Pullman cars boasting classical appellations like Phoenix and Perseus. The ninety minute journey through Kent, 'the Garden of England' allows ample time to savour the Ascot luncheon together with wine before arrival at Folkestone, where holiday-makers and locals alike peer in through the windows at the unashamed decadence within.

The Channel crossing to Boulogne is a relaxed ninety minutes as passengers traverse this busy stretch of water and await their first sighting of land from the comfort of the specially reserved Verandah deck salon on the ferry which bears a Nordic name like Hengist and Horsa.

There on the quayside, drawn up like Grenadier Guards in gleaming Royal blue livery, stand the seventeen cars of The Compagnie Internationale des Wagons-lits et des Grands Express Européens. Waxed mirror bright, they make up the longest passenger train in Europe (400 metres). Excitement grows and normally stoical businessmen can be seen to shout and clap. Formalities are brief and passengers are soon being shown to their compartments in the eleven wagons-lits, which have been expertly restored from the most sumptuous and spacious sleeping cars ever to have run in Europe. Each passenger is presented with an information booklet which lists the many and varied histories of these wagons-lits dating back to 1926. It is not difficult to describe the train as a Hollywood film set running on 136 wheels, miles high from reality.

Soon the Venice Simplon-Orient-Express slips quietly away on the first portion of its journey through five European countries, Paris will be reached in about three hours. This allows ample time to familiarise yourself with your hotel room on wheels and affords your steward the opportunity to take care of passport and customs formalities. Most passengers change for dinner, this is after all, the 'Orient Express', and everyone shares the enthusiasm for the train. For those wishing the first sitting for dinner the two Salon Restaurant cars and Salon Pullman await their guests in all their finery, whilst feverish activity goes on in the galleys. First diners are rewarded with fine views from the dining cars over the rich countryside of the Pas de Calais as the train rushes through steepled villages and storied forests, past vineyards, lakes and battlefields, whilst the passengers who have opted for the second sitting for dinner enjoy this view from the Bar Car, which has been recreated from a first class

The Venice Simplon-Orient-Express lounge on board the cross channel ferry provides a comfortable haven for the elegant passengers during the short voyage across the English Channel.

Restaurant car dating from 1931. The interior is immaculate, with side seating, small stools and coffee tables and even a baby grand piano.

Shortly before Paris passengers will be taking their place in the Restaurant cars for their taste of the world class cuisine, frequently referred to as an absolute gastronomic delight by the many rich and famous people who have already sampled the delights of the journey in time, space and splendour. As evening falls over Paris, the train glides into the Gare de L'Est, this station has witnessed the departure of Grand European Expresses to destinations all over Europe for over one hundred years. The mood continues in the Bar Car, with grand piano playing the night away until the last passenger retires.

The wagons-lits have now been converted from day-time salon configuration to sleeping accommodation and the profusion of linen and blankets soon deadens any noise from the tracks and a relaxed sleep soon follows. An early rise is well rewarded, this time as you peer through the windows; you are greeted with a breathtaking view of the mountains of Switzerland. The snowcapped peaks of Liechtenstein provide a perfect backdrop from which to enjoy a continental breakfast served in your compartment.

Soon the third largest tunnel in Europe, the Arlberg Tunnel, almost 6.5 miles long - separating the Vorarlberg and the Tirol opens on to this most picturesque corner of Austria. The train continues on to Innsbruck and then a splendid lunch is served as the train crosses the Brenner Pass - frontier between Austria and Italy. Passing through historical towns with famous names like Fortezza and Bolzano the train makes its way to Verona - the setting for the ill-fated romance of Romeo and Juliet, Shakespeare's tragic lovers.

Shortly before 7 pm the Venice Simplon-Orient-Express finally crosses the long causeway that connects Mestre, on the mainland, with the island setting of Venice, that unique Italian contribution to civilised city life. The main station of Venice, Santa Lucia, houses a frenzy of porters all ready to whisk your baggage to waiting motorboats or gondolas. You sail past the Palaces of the Doges where the Guardis, Lord Byron and Vivaldi lived, under the Rialto Bridge towards your hotel and days of exploration and romance.

Since the inaugural run, on 28th May 1982, which was sped on its way by the Band of the Coldstream Guards, the passenger list has included English Lords and Ladies, showbiz aristocrats and crowned heads of industry. One passenger was actor Sidney Poitier with his thirty pieces of luggage. On a trip from Venice to Paris, a group of fourteen Arabs celebrated the birthday of a Saudi Princess - the champagne gushed like crude.

The Venice Simplon-Orient-Express received Royal patronage on June 30th 1988 when their Royal Highnesses Prince and Princess Michael of Kent journeyed on the fabled train during its inaugural visit to Vienna, Austria. The theme was nostalgic elegance of the 1920's.

This train, recreated from the rotting ashes of that once great and famous lineage of trains can justly claim to be the Venice Simplon Orient Success, the world's foremost dream train.

Two powerful Austrian electric locomotives pull the 950 tonnes of the Venice Simplon-Orient-Express up to the Arlberg Tunnel, 6.36 miles long at 5,945 feet above sea level.

ORIENT EXPRESS MILESTONES

1883 4th October

Official inauguration of the Express d'Orient from Paris to Constantinople.

1888 13th August

The through run from Paris to Constantinople was established (67 hours 35 minutes), when the railway was completed

1891 The Express d'Orient was officially renamed the Orient Express.

1919 11th April

The Simplon Orient Express from Paris to Istanbul, via Venice was inaugurated under the Treaty of Versailles.

1924 14th November

An all Pullman boat train started from London to Dover.

1926 13th September

Lord Dalziel began the Flèche d'Or from Calais to Paris - an all Pullman service.

1929 15th May

The Golden Arrow was inaugurated from Victoria to Dover to link with the Flèche d'Or at Calais.

1936 14th October

The Night Ferry was inaugurated as a through wagons-lits service from London to Paris and vice versa. (Details in Night Ferry, published 1985 by Jersey Artists).

1939 3rd September

The Golden Arrow, the Night Ferry and the Orient Express were immediately suspended following the declaration of war.

1945 8th May

At the end of World War II, Wagons-Lits had lost 845 cars of their 1939 fleet of 1,738. In Britain, Pullman had owned about 200, of which half were damaged and four completely obliterated.

1946 January

The Simplon Orient Express resumed from Paris to Istanbul.
The Golden Arrow and the Flèche d'Or resumed cross channel operations.

1947 15th December

The Night Ferry was reinstated.

1948 1st January

The railways in Britain were nationalised (but not the Pullman Car Company).

1951 1st June

A new Golden Arrow rake was displayed to celebrate the Festival of Britain.

1961 11th June

The last steam hauled Golden Arrow left Victoria.

1969 Pullman cars were withdrawn from the Flèche d'Or.

1972 30th October

The last run of the Golden Arrow.

1977 19th May

Last departure of the Direct-Orient-Express/Marmara-Express for Istanbul.

8th October

Monte Carlo sale of five Wagons-Lits. Two were bought by James B. Sherwood, President of the Sea Containers Group.

Their Royal Highnesses Prince and Princess Michael of Kent and Lord Frederick Windsor en route to Vienna in Pullman car Phoenix, June 30th, 1988.

1980 31st October

The Night Ferry was withdrawn.

1982 25th May

The inaugural run of the Venice Simplon-Orient-Express from Victoria to Venice.

1982 November

Concorde and the Venice Simplon-Orient-Express join forces for the first time courtesy of Excalibur Holidays.

1983 4th October

The Venice Simplon-Orient-Express celebrated the centennial journey of the first Express d'Orient with a gala departure from London to Paris and on to Venice. The Band of the Coldstream Guards heralded the train on its way from Victoria. On arrival at Paris Gare de l'Est (the first time the train had visited the station) there was a platform party, the train was split in two on adjacent platforms and formed a perfect stage for a truly splendid Parisian party. On arrival in Milan the Bergsaglieri Band played their hunting horns while running the length of the train. Throughout the journey an authentic recreation of the 1833 menu was served to the privileged few who took their place in the history books.

1984 1st July

The Venice Simplon-Orient-Express begins running on the Alpine route via Zurich and Innsbruck through the Arlberg tunnel for the months of July and August. This was to become the train's regular routing with the introduction of the 1985 schedules.

1988 30th June

Inaugural run from London to Vienna. Their Royal Highnesses Prince and Princess Michael of Kent joined a small group of selected passengers to celebrate the new route of the Venice Simplon-Orient-Ex press. The train leaves its traditional route at Innsbruck to travel via Salzburg before arriving at Vienna West-Bahnhof. This route has proved an attractive alternative to regular passengers on the Venice route and will be implemented at various times throughout the year.

Folkestone harbour is the terminus for the Venice Simplon-Orient-Express on the English side of the Channel. Here passengers bound for Venice leave their Pullmans while northbound passengers heading for London join the sumptuous carriages of this all Pullman train and enjoy a typical English afternoon tea.

Travelling from London's Victoria station to the channel port of Folkestone takes but an hour and a half. A splendid three course luncheon is served using the finest English produce in an ambiance of unhurried luxury - the epitome of rail travel in its heyday.

Sleeping car 3482 was built in 1929 and decorated by Maple and ran in famous trains of Europe, including the Train Bleu, Rome Express, Nord Express and laterly the Simplon Orient Express.

Sleeping car 3552, built in 1929 by Enterprises Industrielles Charentaises Aytré, La Rochelle, France was decorated by Nelson and depicts tiger lily marquetry. This car conveyed their Royal Highnesses Prince and Princess Michael of Kent to Vienna during the train's inaugural visit.

Above: The inaugural departure to Vienna. Guests enjoyed a champagne party at Gare de L'Est platform 15, dressed, of course, in true 'Orient Express' style.

Above right: The distinctive blue and cream livery of the bar car recreates the elegance of Europe's great express trains that bore the proud inscription 'Compagnie Internationale DesWagons-Lits Et Des Grands Express Européens'.

In the presence of Their Royal Highnesses
The Prince and Princess Michael of Kent
Mr. James B. Sherwood
Chairman of the Board of Venice Simplon-Orient-Express Ltd.

requests the pleasure of the company of

Gary Buchanan

on the INAUGURAL JOURNEY from London to Vienna of the Venice Simplon-Orient-Express.
The train will depart from Victoria Station, London at 11.00 on Thursday June 30, 1988,
and will arrive at Ostbahnhof, Vienna, at 20.05 on Friday July 1st.

Black tie and 1920's dress preferred.

The cost of £1,000 per person includes all meals on the train.
1 night stay at The Imperial or The Bristol Hotel, Vienna, and scheduled return flight to London.
(Alternative itineraries are available on request).
Proceeds in aid of the Thames Valley Hospice. (President Her Grace the Duchess of Norfolk).

RSVP (Acceptance card enclosed)

Sleeping car 3544, built in 1929 by Enterprises Industrielles Charentaises Aytré, was decorated by René Prou. The car ran in the 'Train Bleu' and 'Rome Express' before the war, was used as a brothel in Limoges during the war and afterwards ran in the Dutch Royal Train and 'Simplon Orient Express'.

In the evening comfortable beds with fine linens are made up by the steward, this transformation after dinner ensures a pleasant rest.

The Italian bar staff will mix a favourite cocktail or deftly serve the finest champagne in the airy surroundings of the bar car - surely this must be the world's most elegant setting for any party.

The bar car - for many the focal hub of the train. Here, elegantly attired passengers enjoy a cocktail or after dinner brandy while listening to the pianist playing requests on the baby grand piano. The revelry frequently lasts well into the night and many interesting liaisons have been formed.

Above: No part of the train has escaped even the minutest attention to detail. Here the mosaic floor of the washroom in Pullman car 'Cygnus' is a masterpiece in art.

Left: inside the continental sleeping car, passengers find an ingeniously designed washing closet. Soft monogrammed towels, fragrant soaps and designer colognes all add to the cachet of the Venice Simplon-Orient-Express.

Meals on the Venice Simplon-Orient-Express are a truly elegant occasion. Served in the sumptuous surroundings of the two Restaurant cars and Pullman car. Here the 'Etoile du Nord' Restaurant car No. 4110, built in 1927 with marquetry panels made of many coloured woods depicting baskets of flowers awaits its well attired diners.

The Oriental dining car No. 4095, built in 1927 boasts distinctive black lacquer panels that are so redolent of the great era of the 1920's.

The Pullman car 4141 reflects an age of romance with the René Lalique glass panels depicting 'Bacchanalian Maidens' - what better setting to celebrate a honeymoon, anniversary or simply to indulge the inner self.

Destination - Venice. The gondolas epitomise this quintessential Renaissance city. Looking from St Marks Square across the lagoon to San Giorgio Maggiore on the left and Guidecca on the right, home of the Cipriani Hotel.

A marquetry landscape panel from Pullman car 'Audrey', built in 1932 for the Brighton Belle. This car has carried Her Majesty Queen Elizabeth II, Her Majesty Queen Elizabeth the Queen Mother and His Royal Highness The Duke of Edinburgh.

A detail from the etched glass panel and tulip light in the bar car. The Venice Simplon-Orient-Express exudes Art Deco luxury.

The full majesty of the seventeen coach express is captured in this Alpine setting. The sleeping cars are in two sections at either end of the train with the restaurant, Pullman and bar cars in the centre of the train almost half a kilometre in length.

Many passengers take a special pride in dressing in period costume for a journey on the Venice Simplon-Orient-Express. Designer luggage, roaring twenties dresses and grand tour linens all help to enhance the special atmosphere created by this very special train.

MENU
LE DINER

Côtelettes de Turbot à la Crème de Tourteaux
Steamed turbot and crab meat with chives and lobster sauce
* * *

Coeur de Filet au Foie Gras et Brisures de Truffes
Sautéed fillet of beef with "Foie Gras" and truffles

Mosaïque de Légumes
Selection of vegetables

Pommes Château
Roast potatoes
* * *

Plateau de Fromages de France
Fine French cheeses
* * *

Cèpe Gascon aux Marrons glacés
Chocolate meringue and chestnut ice
* * *

Mignardises
* * *

Café de Colombie - Colombian Coffee

ND.8709.900   Chef de Cuisine: Christian Bodiguel

92

Above: Chef Christian Bodiguel prepares some of the most delicate dishes ever served on a train for patrons on the Venice Simplon-Orient-Express. Each dish is individually prepared and presented by deft waiters. A specially selected wine list gives the perfect compliment to such a memorable meal.

Above left: Some of the most romantic journeys aboard the Venice Simplon-Orient-Express are made in winter. The Arlberg Pass is in the grip of winter reflecting the warmth of the sleeping cars of Europe's longest train.

Below left: Descending towards Switzerland, afternoon tea is served in the privacy of the cabins as the legendary express thunders past ever changing scenery.

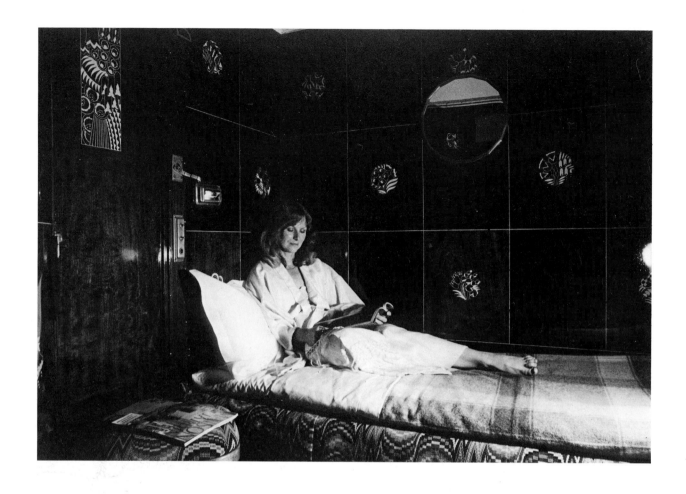

Above: Taking a double cabin for sole use is really travelling in style. Inter-communicating doors between pairs of cabins allow the ultimate in 'grand style' travelling luxury. As the mighty express thunders across Europe, passengers dress for dinner sporting classical elegance or recreating the night of railways heyday - the twenties and thirties.

Right: Brightly polished mahogany and tasteful fabrics are evident in the Pullman cars. Here car 'Cygnus' reflects the tranquillity and style that is so much part of the Venice Simplon-Orient-Express experience.

ACKNOWLEDGEMENTS

In this necessarily brief account of Concorde, Queen Elizabeth 2 and the Venice Simplon-Orient-Express, I have had the kindest co-operation from the following, to whom, along with their organisations where applicable, I should like to say thank you for either their time or patience, possibly both and certainly their generosity;

Captain Brian Walpole, George Blundell-Pound, Hilary Genin and Ron Wilson of British Airways, Captain Alan Bennell, Eric Flounders and George Law of Cunard Line, Shirley Sherwood, John Roozemond, Sally Humphries and Isabella Donnelly of the Venice Simplon-Orient-Express, Glyn Genin of the Financial Times, Wally Pyemont of Image in Industry, Ralph Rogers of World Backgrounds, Chris Perkins, Adrian Meredith and Mike Moon. Not forgetting Denis Orient for his valuable assistance in providing refreshing ideas in the preparation of 'Dream Voyages'. My publisher, George Behrend, I commend for his patience and encouragement and to anybody I may have inadvertently omitted, please accept my heart felt thanks.

ILLUSTRATION ACKNOWLEDGEMENTS

Photographs were kindly supplied by the following;
Adrian Meredith Photography
British Airways Photographic Library
Cunard Line Ltd
Financial Times
Image in Industry
Ocean Pictures Ltd
Chris Perkins Photography
World Backgrounds
Venice Simplon-Orient-Express

plus authors collection.

Copyright for the illustration of Concorde, Q.E.2 and the Red Arrows belongs to Arthur Gibson. All other copyrights are the property of the supplier.
Cover design by David Postle and Eric Bottomley.